THIS JOURNAL BELONGS TO

_____

AFFIRMATIONS:

Affirmations are short phrases to say to help emotionally support and encourage yourself.

◆ Today will be a great day. ◆ I will do my best today.

◆ I believe in my dreams. ◆ I believe in myself. ◆ I am only human.

◆ I am loved. ◆ I am brave. ◆ I am enough. ◆ I can forgive others.

◆ I am thankful to be me. ◆ I am only human.

◆ I am brave enough to be myself.

◆ I choose to learn from my mistakes. ◆ I forgive my mistakes.

◆ I am proud of myself and my accomplishments.

◆ The challenges that I face help me grow stronger.

ABOUT ME

MY FAMILY

MY PORTRAIT

MY FAVORITE THINGS

Color

Animal

Place

Hobby

Book

Movie

Season

Sport/Game

Draw a picture of 2
of your favorite things.

DATE : _____   TODAY I FEEL... 😃 😐 😟 😠 ⚪

3 THINGS I'M

GRATEFUL

FOR

1. _____
2. _____
3. _____

What motivates you?

_____
_____
_____
_____
_____
_____
_____
_____
_____
_____
_____
_____
_____
_____
_____

AFFIRMATIONS

DATE : _____ TODAY I FEEL... 😃 😐 😟 😠 ○

3 THINGS I'M
GRATEFUL
FOR

1. _____
2. _____
3. _____

Write about something in the
room that you are grateful for.

_____
_____
_____
_____
_____
_____
_____
_____
_____
_____
_____
_____
_____
_____

AFFIRMATIONS

DATE : _____ TODAY I FEEL... 😃 😶 😔 😠 ◯

3 THINGS I'M

GRATEFUL
FOR

1. _____
2. _____
3. _____

What is your greatest talent?

_____
_____
_____
_____
_____
_____
_____
_____
_____
_____
_____
_____
_____

AFFIRMATIONS

DATE: _____ TODAY I FEEL... 😃 😐 ☹️ 😠 ◯

3 THINGS I'M
GRATEFUL
FOR

1. _____
2. _____
3. _____

What always puts you in a good mood?

_____
_____
_____
_____
_____
_____
_____
_____
_____
_____
_____
_____
_____
_____

AFFIRMATIONS

DATE : _____   TODAY I FEEL... 😀 😐 😞 😠 ◯

3 THINGS I'M

GRATEFUL

FOR

1. _____
2. _____
3. _____

Write about a favorite memory.
What does it mean to you?

_____
_____
_____
_____
_____
_____
_____
_____
_____
_____

_____

_____

_____

_____

_____

_____

AFFIRMATIONS

DATE : _____ TODAY I FEEL... 😃 😐 ☹️ 😠 ○

3 THINGS I'M
GRATEFUL FOR

1. _____
2. _____
3. _____

What's your greatest achievement?

_____
_____
_____
_____
_____
_____
_____
_____
_____
_____
_____
_____
_____
_____

AFFIRMATIONS

DATE : _____ TODAY I FEEL... 😀 😐 🙁 😠 ◯

3 THINGS I'M
GRATEFUL
FOR

1. _____
2. _____
3. _____

Write something unique about yourself.
How does this help you?

_____
_____
_____
_____
_____
_____
_____
_____
_____

_____
_____
_____
_____
_____
_____
_____

AFFIRMATIONS

DATE : —————— TODAY I FEEL... 😀 😐 😟 😠 ◯

3 THINGS I'M
GRATEFUL
FOR

1. _____
2. _____
3. _____

Imagine your perfect day. What does it look like?

_____
_____
_____
_____
_____
_____
_____
_____
_____
_____
_____
_____
_____
_____
_____
_____

AFFIRMATIONS

DATE : _____   TODAY I FEEL... 😀 😐 😟 😠 ⚪

3 THINGS I'M

GRATEFUL

FOR

1. _____

2. _____

3. _____

What are you most proud of that you've done?

_____
_____
_____
_____
_____
_____
_____
_____
_____
_____
_____
_____
_____

AFFIRMATIONS

DATE : ———————— TODAY I FEEL... 😄 😐 ☹️ 😠 ◯

3 THINGS I'M
GRATEFUL
FOR

1. _____
2. _____
3. _____

Write five statements about yourself that start with "Iam..."
Which one of these statements is your favorite?

_____
_____
_____
_____
_____
_____
_____
_____
_____
_____
_____
_____
_____
_____

AFFIRMATIONS

13

DATE : —————— TODAY I FEEL... 😁 😀 😞 😠 ◯

3 THINGS I'M

GRATEFUL

FOR

1. _____

2. _____

3. _____

Write about a time you're NOT grateful for?
Did anything good come out of it?

_____

_____

_____

_____

_____

_____

_____

_____

_____

_____

_____

_____

_____

_____

_____

AFFIRMATIONS

DATE : ———— TODAY I FEEL... 😄 😐 🙁 😠 ◯

3 THINGS I'M
GRATEFUL
FOR

1. _____
2. _____
3. _____

What good thing happened today?

_____
_____
_____
_____
_____
_____
_____
_____
_____
_____
_____
_____
_____
_____
_____

AFFIRMATIONS

DATE : _____ TODAY I FEEL... 😃 😐 😞 😠 ○

3 THINGS I'M
GRATEFUL
FOR

1. _____
2. _____
3. _____

How do you feel when you are confident?
What emotions do you experience?

_____
_____
_____
_____
_____
_____
_____
_____
_____
_____
_____
_____
_____
_____
_____

AFFIRMATIONS

DATE : —————— TODAY I FEEL... 😀 😐 🙁 😠 ○

3 THINGS I'M
GRATEFUL
FOR

1. _____
2. _____
3. _____

Who's the most positive person you know? Do you enjoy being around them? How do you think you could be more like them?

_____
_____
_____
_____
_____
_____
_____
_____
_____
_____
_____
_____
_____
_____
_____

AFFIRMATIONS

DATE : _____ TODAY I FEEL... 😀 😐 😞 😠 ◯

3 THINGS I'M

GRATEFUL

FOR

1. _____
2. _____
3. _____

What is your favorite part of nature?

_____
_____
_____
_____
_____
_____
_____
_____
_____
_____
_____
_____
_____
_____
_____
_____

AFFIRMATIONS

DATE : —————— TODAY I FEEL... 😃 😐 😞 😠 ○

3 THINGS I'M
GRATEFUL
FOR

1. _____
2. _____
3. _____

What does self-esteem mean to you?
How does feeling good about yourself help you in your daily life?

_____
_____
_____
_____
_____
_____
_____
_____
_____
_____
_____
_____
_____
_____
_____
_____
_____
_____

AFFIRMATIONS

DATE : —————— TODAY I FEEL... 😃 😐 🙁 😠 ◌

3 THINGS I'M

GRATEFUL

FOR

1. _____

2. _____

3. _____

What do you think you could do to be more positive
in your daily life? Even the small things matter!

_____

_____

_____

_____

_____

_____

_____

_____

_____

_____

_____

_____

_____

_____

AFFIRMATIONS

DATE : ———— TODAY I FEEL... 😃 😐 😞 😠 ○

3 THINGS I'M
GRATEFUL
FOR

1. _____
2. _____
3. _____

What do you think would be the best job to have?

_____
_____
_____
_____
_____
_____
_____
_____
_____
_____
_____
_____
_____
_____
_____
_____
_____
_____

AFFIRMATIONS

3 THINGS I'M

GRATEFUL
FOR

1. _____
2. _____
3. _____

Write about a person you admire. What qualities do you like most about them? How can you be more like them?

_____
_____
_____
_____
_____
_____
_____
_____
_____
_____
_____
_____
_____
_____
_____

AFFIRMATIONS

DATE : —————— TODAY I FEEL... 😃 😐 😔 😠 ⚪

3 THINGS I'M
GRATEFUL
FOR

1. _____

2. _____

3. _____

Many people say that when they think more positively they feel much better, even on their bad days. Why do you think that this is?

_____
_____
_____
_____
_____
_____
_____
_____
_____
_____
_____
_____
_____
_____

AFFIRMATIONS

DATE : ———————— TODAY I FEEL... 😃 😐 😞 😠 ◯

3 THINGS I'M

GRATEFUL FOR

1. _____
2. _____
3. _____

Do you have a favorite author or book? Write about it.

_____
_____
_____
_____
_____
_____
_____
_____
_____
_____
_____
_____
_____
_____
_____

AFFIRMATIONS

DATE : ——————— TODAY I FEEL... 😃 😐 😞 😠 ◯

3 THINGS I'M
GRATEFUL
FOR

1. _____
2. _____
3. _____

What makes you feel like a strong and capable person?

_____
_____
_____
_____
_____
_____
_____
_____
_____
_____
_____
_____
_____
_____
_____

AFFIRMATIONS

DATE : ——————— TODAY I FEEL... 😀 😐 🙁 😠 ◯

3 THINGS I'M

GRATEFUL

FOR

1. _____
2. _____
3. _____

What would you say to your very best friend if they were feeling down? How can you extend some of this compassion to yourself?

_____
_____
_____
_____
_____
_____
_____
_____
_____
_____
_____
_____
_____
_____

AFFIRMATIONS

DATE : —————— TODAY I FEEL... 😄 😐 😟 😠 ◯

3 THINGS I'M
GRATEFUL
FOR

1. _____
2. _____
3. _____

Make a list of people you're glad to have in your life.
How could you show them what they mean to you on a daily basis?

_____
_____
_____
_____
_____
_____
_____
_____
_____
_____
_____
_____
_____
_____
_____

AFFIRMATIONS

3 THINGS I'M

GRATEFUL

FOR

1. _____
2. _____
3. _____

What makes you feel strong?

AFFIRMATIONS

DATE : ———————— TODAY I FEEL... 😃 😐 😟 😠 ◯

3 THINGS I'M
GRATEFUL
FOR

1. _____
2. _____
3. _____

What is your favorite animal? What do you like about it?

_____
_____
_____
_____
_____
_____
_____
_____
_____
_____
_____
_____
_____
_____
_____

AFFIRMATIONS

DATE : ——————— TODAY I FEEL... 😃 😐 ☹️ 😠 ◯

3 THINGS I'M
GRATEFUL
FOR

1. _____
2. _____
3. _____

What is something you're grateful for that
you have now, but didn't have a year ago?

_____
_____
_____
_____
_____
_____
_____
_____
_____

_____
_____
_____
_____
_____
_____
_____

AFFIRMATIONS

DATE : ———————— TODAY I FEEL... 😀 😐 😞 😠 ◯

3 THINGS I'M
GRATEFUL
FOR

1. _____
2. _____
3. _____

What kind of things can damage your self-esteem?
Why should you avoid these activities?

_____
_____
_____
_____
_____
_____
_____
_____
_____
_____
_____
_____
_____
_____
_____

AFFIRMATIONS

DATE : _____ TODAY I FEEL... 😃 😐 😞 😠 ◯

3 THINGS I'M GRATEFUL FOR

1. _____
2. _____
3. _____

What is your favorite subject in school? Why do you like it?

_____
_____
_____
_____
_____
_____
_____
_____
_____
_____
_____
_____
_____
_____

AFFIRMATIONS

DATE : _____ TODAY I FEEL... 😄 😐 🙁 😠 ◯

3 THINGS I'M
GRATEFUL
FOR

1. _____
2. _____
3. _____

Which person in your past are you most grateful for?
What did they teach you?

_____
_____
_____
_____
_____
_____
_____
_____
_____
_____
_____
_____
_____
_____
_____
_____

AFFIRMATIONS

DATE : ——————— TODAY I FEEL... 😀 😐 😞 😠 ◯

3 THINGS I'M

GRATEFUL

FOR

1. _____
2. _____
3. _____

Write about a time that you felt recognized and appreciated.
Why is it important to extend this feeling to ourselves and others?

_____
_____
_____
_____
_____
_____
_____
_____
_____
_____
_____
_____
_____
_____

AFFIRMATIONS

34

DATE : ———————   TODAY I FEEL... 😃 😐 ☹️ 😠 ◯

3 THINGS I'M
GRATEFUL
FOR

1. _____
2. _____
3. _____

What does self-esteem mean to you?

_____
_____
_____
_____
_____
_____
_____
_____
_____
_____
_____
_____
_____
_____
_____

AFFIRMATIONS

DATE : _____ TODAY I FEEL... 😃 😐 🙁 😠 ○

3 THINGS I'M

GRATEFUL

FOR

1. _____
2. _____
3. _____

Write about a person or place that makes you feel safe.

_____
_____
_____
_____
_____
_____
_____
_____
_____
_____
_____

AFFIRMATIONS

DATE : _____ TODAY I FEEL... 😃 😐 ☹️ 😠 ○

3 THINGS I'M **GRATEFUL** FOR

1. _____
2. _____
3. _____

What do you think other people see when they look at you?

_____
_____
_____
_____
_____
_____
_____
_____
_____
_____
_____
_____
_____
_____

AFFIRMATIONS

DATE : ——————— TODAY I FEEL... 😁 😐 🙁 😡 ◯

3 THINGS I'M

GRATEFUL
FOR

1. _____
2. _____
3. _____

On our bad days, it's important to remember
that everyone makes mistakes, and we are only human.
When was there a time that you could have used this reminder?

_____
_____
_____
_____
_____
_____
_____
_____
_____
_____
_____
_____
_____
_____

AFFIRMATIONS

DATE : _____ TODAY I FEEL... 😃 😐 😣 😡 ◯

3 THINGS I'M
GRATEFUL
FOR

1. _____
2. _____
3. _____

How do you know that you've been successful?
What does it feel like?

_____
_____
_____
_____
_____
_____
_____
_____

_____
_____
_____
_____
_____
_____
_____

AFFIRMATIONS

DATE : ———— TODAY I FEEL... 😃 😐 😞 😠 ◯

3 THINGS I'M
GRATEFUL
FOR

1. _____
2. _____
3. _____

What is your favorite activity to do outdoors?

_____
_____
_____
_____
_____
_____
_____
_____
_____
_____
_____
_____
_____
_____
_____

AFFIRMATIONS

DATE : ———————— TODAY I FEEL... 😀 😐 ☹️ 😠 ◯

3 THINGS I'M

GRATEFUL

FOR

1. _____

2. _____

3. _____

What do you know that you are grateful for?

_____

_____

_____

_____

_____

_____

_____

_____

_____

_____

_____

_____

_____

_____

_____

_____

AFFIRMATIONS

DATE : ——————— TODAY I FEEL... 😃 😐 😟 😠 ◯

3 THINGS I'M
GRATEFUL
FOR

1. _____
2. _____
3. _____

Make a list of ten things you like about yourself.
If you find this difficult, why do you think that might be?
How could you change your outlook?

_____
_____
_____
_____
_____
_____
_____
_____
_____
_____
_____
_____
_____
_____
_____

AFFIRMATIONS

DATE : ——————— TODAY I FEEL... 😄 😐 😟 😠 ◯

3 THINGS I'M
GRATEFUL
FOR

1. _____
2. _____
3. _____

Write a list of five things you would do if you were not afraid.
How would it impact your life?

_____
_____
_____
_____
_____
_____
_____
_____
_____
_____
_____
_____
_____
_____
_____
_____
_____
_____
_____

AFFIRMATIONS

DATE : —————— TODAY I FEEL... 😄 😐 😞 😠 ⚪

3 THINGS I'M
GRATEFUL
FOR

1. _____
2. _____
3. _____

What is the best compliment you've ever received?
How did it make you feel?

_____
_____
_____
_____
_____
_____
_____
_____
_____
_____
_____
_____
_____
_____

AFFIRMATIONS

DATE : —————— TODAY I FEEL... 😃 😐 😞 😠 ○

3 THINGS I'M
GRATEFUL
FOR

1. _____
2. _____
3. _____

What is the best gift that you've ever received?

_____
_____
_____
_____
_____
_____
_____
_____
_____
_____
_____
_____
_____

AFFIRMATIONS

DATE : ——————— TODAY I FEEL... 😃 😐 😞 😠 ⚪

3 THINGS I'M
GRATEFUL
FOR

1. _____
2. _____
3. _____

What made you smile today?

_____
_____
_____
_____
_____
_____
_____
_____
_____
_____

_____
_____
_____
_____
_____
_____
_____
_____

AFFIRMATIONS

DATE : ———————— TODAY I FEEL... 😃 😐 😞 😠 ◯

3 THINGS I'M **GRATEFUL** FOR

1. _____
2. _____
3. _____

Think about someone you admire.
What do you have in common?

_____
_____
_____
_____
_____
_____
_____
_____
_____
_____
_____
_____
_____
_____
_____
_____
_____

AFFIRMATIONS

DATE : —————— TODAY I FEEL... 😀 😐 😞 😠 ⚬

3 THINGS I'M

GRATEFUL

FOR

1. _____

2. _____

3. _____

What is your biggest goal?
How can you help yourself achieve it?

_____
_____
_____
_____
_____
_____
_____
_____
_____
_____
_____
_____
_____
_____
_____
_____

AFFIRMATIONS

DATE : ——————— TODAY I FEEL... 😀 😵 😟 😠 ○

3 THINGS I'M
GRATEFUL
FOR

1. _____
2. _____
3. _____

What is your favorite smell?

_____
_____
_____
_____
_____
_____
_____
_____
_____
_____
_____
_____
_____
_____

AFFIRMATIONS

DATE : _____ TODAY I FEEL... 😄 😐 😟 😠 ◯

3 THINGS I'M

GRATEFUL

FOR

1. _____
2. _____
3. _____

What would you do if there was nothing stopping you?
What can you learn from this?

_____
_____
_____
_____
_____
_____
_____
_____
_____
_____
_____
_____
_____
_____
_____
_____

AFFIRMATIONS

DATE : —————— TODAY I FEEL... 😃 😐 ☹️ 😠 ◯

3 THINGS I'M **GRATEFUL** FOR

1. _____
2. _____
3. _____

What is your favorite song? What does it mean to you?

_____
_____
_____
_____
_____
_____
_____
_____
_____
_____
_____

_____
_____
_____
_____
_____
_____
_____
_____
_____

AFFIRMATIONS

Look online and fill this page with quotes about self-confidence.
Look back on it when you're feeling down.

Color Walk

Take a walk outside following objects of your favorite color.
Write about your experience.

_____

_____

_____

_____

_____

_____

_____

_____

Did you find somewhere new?
Bring back a souvenir! Paste it here!

Smile for a Day

Try to wear a smile for the entire day.
Write down anything different you notice.

Draw your self-portrait here.

Mirror, Mirror

What do you see when you look in the mirror?
Fill out this space! When I look in the mirror I see...

Pay it Forward

Donate something you no longer use.
Think about what it meant to you, and then think
about what it might mean to someone else in the future.

What did you decide to donate? Why is it important?

Draw or paste a picture of the item here.

Award Ceremony

Pretend you are receiving an extremely prestigious award.

Write the speech you would give, including all the amazing things you would want your fans to know about you.

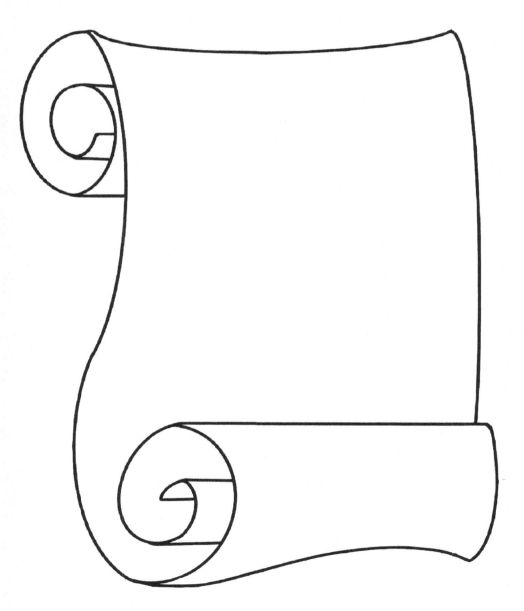

Recharge: Do something nice for yourself.

Take a bath, watch a movie, read a book;
do something you enjoy for at least an hour.

How did you spend your time?

DIY Affirmations

Affirmations are short phrases to say to help emotionally support and encourage yourself.

Write yourself some affirmations to say at in the morning.

Examples

I am stronger than I think.
I am myself and that is enough.

Vision Board

Use magazines or newspapers to cut out pictures or words
that represent what you want your ideal life to look like.
Glue them here and let this page serve as a vision board.

Gratitude Scavenger Hunt!

Find the following items: Something that makes you smile, somthing to make someone else smile, something you like to smell, something that is your favorite color, and something that is useful to you.

Write them all down here.

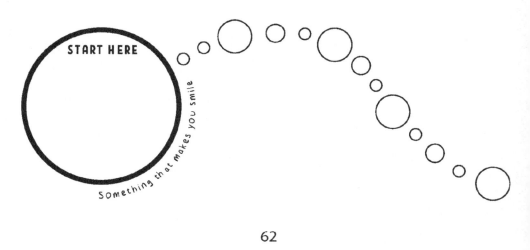

START HERE

Something that makes you smile

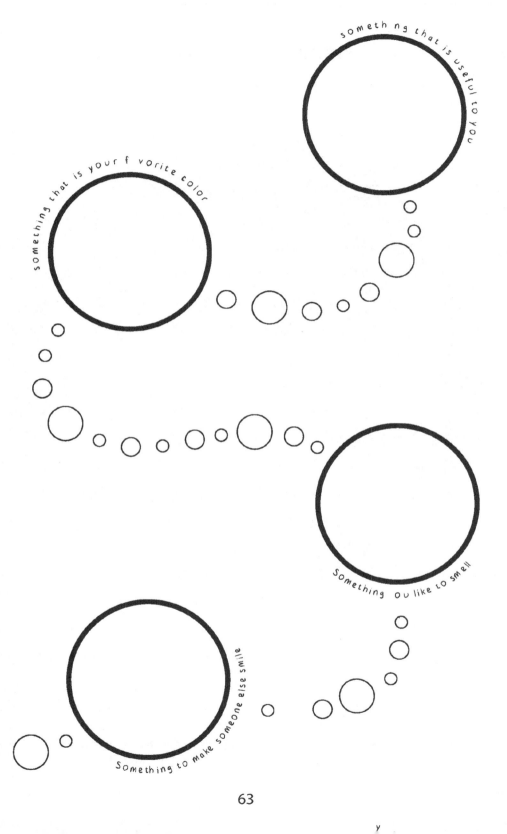

Mandala Motivation

Color this mandala design.

Mandalas are representations of the world in Buddhist and Hindu culture. They use it as an aid to meditate and become spiritually stronger. In addition to this, the mandalas are made of only sand, leaving such beautiful work to be washed away. This represents the temporary nature of most things, encouraging us to embrace the moment and remember that nothing is permanent. While coloring your mandala, give yourself permission to be imperfect.

Random Acts of Kindness

Leave nice notes for **the people you care about** to find.
Cut the notes out and give them to people.

Negative to Positive Playlist

Think about how you feel when you're down. Do you hear the same bad thoughts over and over again? Write down what some of the thoughts on this negative thought playlist are.

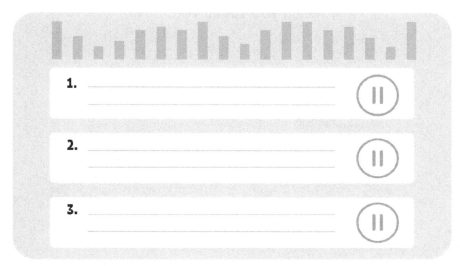

1. _____

2. _____

3. _____

How can you re-frame these to make a new, positive playlist? For example, instead of thinking that your friends no longer want to hang out because you're busy on Saturday, think that your friends will understand, and ask to hang out on Sunday instead.

1. _____

2. _____

3. _____

Recharge: Do something nice for yourself.

Take a bath, watch a movie, read a book;
do something you enjoy for at least an hour.

How did you spend your time?

Pay it Forward

Compliment **3 strangers** you see.
How did it make them feel? How did it make you feel?

1.

_____

_____

_____

_____

_____

2.

_____

_____

_____

_____

_____

3.

_____

_____

_____

_____

_____

Lending Library

Find a book that you really liked, but no longer read or want. Take a sticky note and write what you liked about it or what was special about it to you on the inside cover. Leave it in a public place for someone else to find and enjoy!

Write about it here.

Title:

Color Walk

Take a walk outside following objects of your favorite color.
Write about your experience.

_____

_____

_____

_____

_____

_____

_____

_____

_____

Did you find somewhere new?
Bring back a souvenir! Paste it here!

Pay it Forward

Compliment **3 friends** today.
How did it make them feel? How did it make you feel?

1. _____
_____
_____
_____
_____

2. _____
_____
_____
_____
_____

3. _____
_____
_____
_____
_____

Random Acts of Kindness

Leave nice notes in a public place for **strangers** to find.

Recharge: Do something nice for yourself.

Take a bath, watch a movie, read a book;
do something you enjoy for at least an hour.

How did you spend your time?

Shield of Self Love

Fill out this shield with things you love about yourself.
Let it protect you from negative thoughts on your bad days.

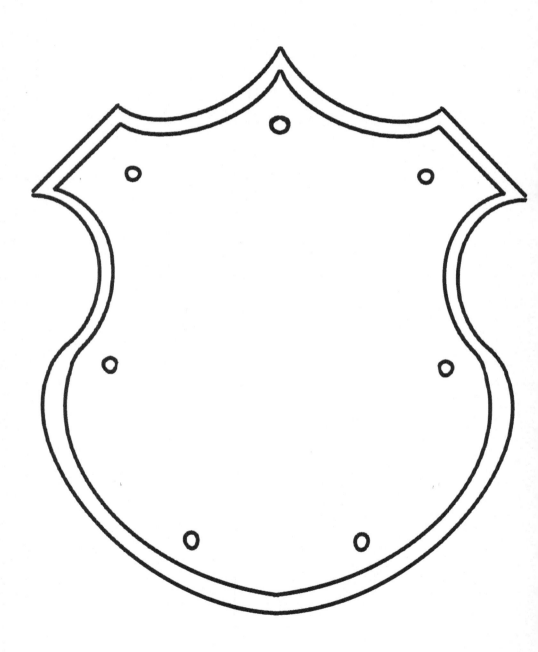

Considering Control

Think about what is in your control. What can you manage? You can only control yourself; your behaviors, your reactions to situations, your attitude, the way you talk to others, and the way you talk to yourself. In the space outside the hand, write things that you cannot control. Understand this, and let go of your worry.

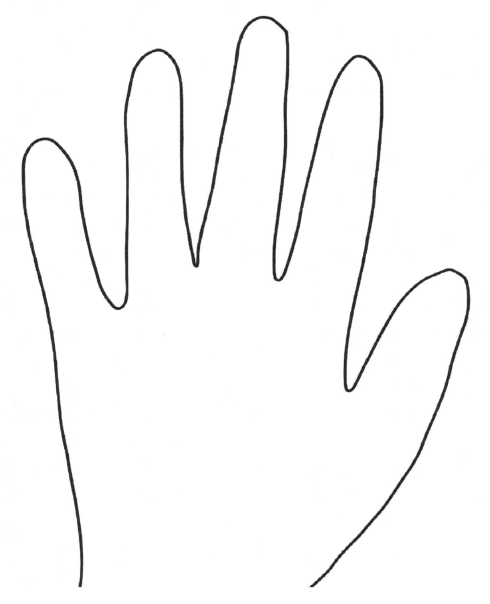

Thankfulness A-Z

Write one thing you are thankful for starting
with each letter of the alphabet.

A

C

E

B

D

F

G

I

K

S

H

J

L

M

O

Q

N

P

R

T

V

X

Z

U

W

Y

Gratitude Rocks

Paint rocks and create a rock garden with art. Alternatively, you could leave some rocks in a park or public place for others to find.

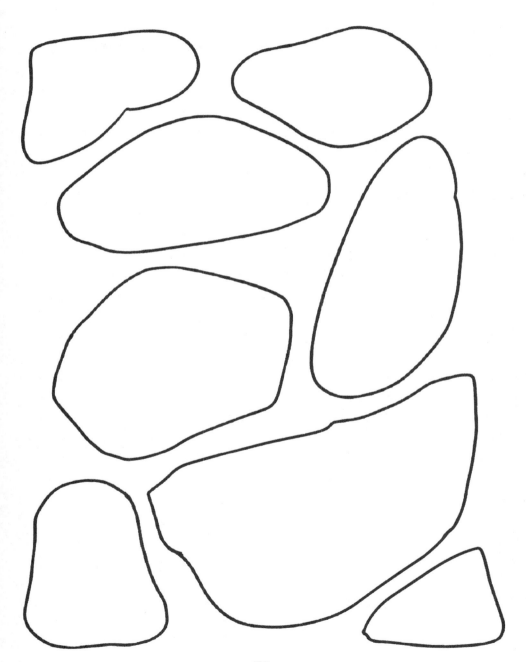

Pay it Forward

Donate something you no longer use.
Think about what it meant to you, and then think
about what it might mean to someone else in the future.

What did you decide to donate? Why is it important?

Draw or paste a picture of the item here.

Random Acts of Kindness

Leave a nice note in a public place for a stranger to find.

Pay it Forward

Compliment **3 people** today.
How did it make them feel? How did it make you feel?

1. _____
   _____
   _____
   _____
   _____
   _____

2. _____
   _____
   _____
   _____
   _____
   _____

3. _____
   _____
   _____
   _____
   _____
   _____

Smile for a Day

Try to wear a smile for the entire day.
Write down anything different you notice.

Did this make you smile? Did it Feel good?
Tap into that feeling and watch the day change even a little bit!

Recharge: Do something nice for yourself.

Take a bath, watch a movie, read a book;
do something you enjoy for at least an hour.

How did you spend your time?

DIY Affirmations

Affirmations are short phrases to say to help
emotionally support and encourage yourself.

Write yourself some affirmations to say at night.

Examples

I am stronger than I think.
I am myself and that is enough.

Lending Library

Find a book that you really liked, but no longer read or want. Take a sticky note and write what you liked about it or what was special about it to you on the inside cover. Leave it in a public place for someone else to find and enjoy!

Self-Love Rocks

Paint rocks and create a rock garden with kind words to yourself and others. Write some of those words here.

Love

Hope

Grateful

Thoughtful

Shield of Self Love

Fill out this shield with things you love about yourself.
Let it protect you from negative thoughts on your bad days.

Gratitude Scavenger Hunt!

Find the following items: Something that makes you smile, somthing to make someone else smile, something you like to smell, something that is your favorite color, and something that is useful to you.

Write them all down here.

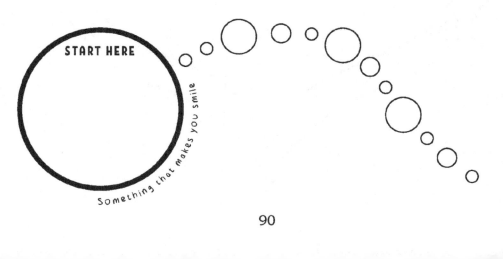

START HERE

Something that makes you smile

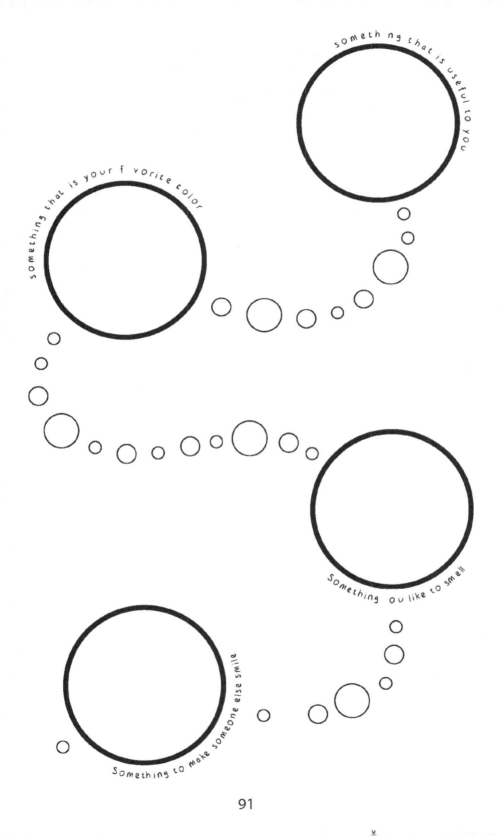

Pay it Forward

Compliment **3 strangers** you see today.
How did it make them feel? How did it make you feel?

1. _____
_____
_____
_____
_____

2. _____
_____
_____
_____
_____

3. _____
_____
_____
_____
_____

Write a letter

Write a letter to someone you haven't talked to in a while.

Recharge: Do something nice for yourself.

Take a bath, watch a movie, read a book;
do something you enjoy for at least an hour.

How did you spend your time?

Vision Board

Use magazines or newspapers to cut out pictures or words that represent what you want your ideal life to look like. Glue them here and let this page serve as a vision board.

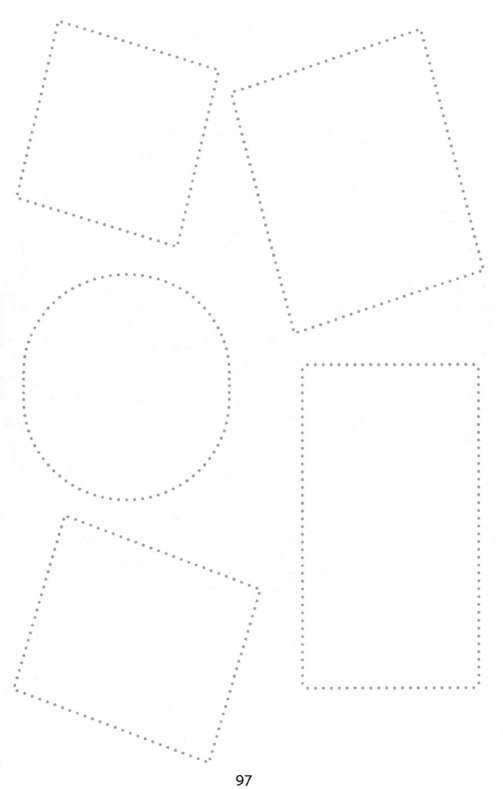

Mandala Motivation

Color this mandala design.

Mandalas are representations of the world in Buddhist and Hindu culture. They use it as an aid to meditate and become spiritually stronger. In addition to this, the mandalas are made of only sand, leaving such beautiful work to be washed away. This represents the temporary nature of most things, encouraging us to embrace the moment and remember that nothing is permanent. While coloring your mandala, give yourself permission to be imperfect.

Write a letter

Write a letter to someone you haven't talked to in a while. Think about all the ways they changed you for the better and made you grow, and all the things you are grateful for.

Made in the USA
Coppell, TX
31 October 2021